First published by Parragon in 2011

Parragon
Queen Street House
4 Queen Street
Bath BA1 1HE, UK

ISBN 978-1-4454-2084-4

Printed in Poland

Adapted by Lisa Marsoli

Illustrated by Caroline LaVelle Egan, Scott Tilley,
Andrew Phillipson and Seung Beom Kim

Bath · New York · Singapore · Hong Kong · Cologne · Delhi
Melbourne · Amsterdam · Johannesburg · Auckland · Shenzhen

British secret agent Finn McMissile had received a distress call from a fellow agent. Finn travelled to the agent's location in the middle of the Pacific Ocean. He was stowed away on an attack ship that was heading towards an oil derrick.

Using his grappling hooks and magnetic wheel armour, Finn silently drove up the side of the oil derrick. As he reached the upper levels, he realized there were hundreds of oil derricks surrounding him!

Finn hid inside the derrick and observed a wanted criminal named Professor Z. Beside the Professor and his crew was a special TV camera. Then Finn saw his fellow agent. He had been crushed and cubed into scrap metal!

Suddenly, Professor Z spotted Finn and sent his gang after him. When they cornered Finn, he leaped off the derrick, turned into a submarine and escaped!

Meanwhile, in the town of Radiator Springs, Mater had called all his friends together to welcome home his best friend, Lightning McQueen. The famous race car had just won the Hudson Hornet Memorial Piston Cup.

Lightning had finally arrived and Mater was overjoyed to see him.

Later that night at the Wheel Well restaurant, Mater called in to a TV show. He defended Lightning against the egotistical Italian race car, Francesco Bernoulli who swore he was faster than Lightning.

Soon, Lightning was on the phone. He agreed to race against Francesco in the World Grand Prix – a three-event race hosted by former oil tycoon, Sir Miles Axlerod.

Mater, Luigi, Guido, Fillmore and Sarge all offered to be Lightning's pit crew. Soon "Team Lightning McQueen" headed to the first World Grand Prix event in Japan!

Lightning and his friends had a fantastic time sightseeing in the city of Tokyo. There were skyscrapers, neon lights, Kabuki theatre and high-tech gadgets!

They all went to a fancy welcome party.

Finn McMissile and another British agent, Holley Shiftwell, were also there. They were looking for an American agent who had some top-secret information for them.

Mater embarrassed Lightning at the party by leaking oil on the floor right in front of Miles Axlerod!

Lightning sent Mater to the bathroom to clean up.
Professor Z's goons, Grem and Acer, had
cornered the American agent, Rod "Torque" Redline
in the bathroom. When Mater came out of his stall,
the agent secretly stuck the device he was supposed
to give to the British spies on Mater.

Later, Professor Z questioned Torque, and guessed that the American agent had passed the device to Mater. The Professor sent Grem and Acer to find the tow truck and get back the device.

21

On the day of the race, Finn and Holley watched all the cars fill up with a new alternative fuel called Allinol. Miles Axlerod, the inventor of Allinol, was hosting the World Grand Prix to introduce the fuel to the public.

Grem and Acer aimed Professor Z's camera at one of the race cars. The camera emitted a beam of radiation that made the Allinol in the car boil and explode!

Then Acer tried to grab Mater.

Holley guided him out of the pits to safety. Mater happily
followed Holley's instructions. He thought he was meeting her
for a date!

Suddenly, Grem and Acer started to close in on Mater –
but Finn jumped in to save him. Mater thought the fight was
the best karate demonstration he had ever seen!

LAP 00 TIME 00:00

Back at the race, Lightning lost to Francesco Bernoulli. Lightning was upset that Mater had given him such bad racing tips.

Reporters surrounded Miles Axlerod and asked him if Allinol was to blame for the engine blowouts during the race. He insisted his fuel was absolutely safe.

Meanwhile, Mater had returned to the pit garage and was trying to explain to Lightning what had just happened.

But Lightning didn't believe him. He was angry with Mater for making him lose the race.

Mater felt terrible. He left a goodbye note for Lightning and went to the airport to fly home.

Finn McMissile, who was disguised as an airport security guard, was waiting for him. Finn still thought Mater was a secret agent.

Soon Grem and Acer showed up and tried to capture Mater again. Holley saved Mater and Finn from the attack by whisking them off on a spy plane named Siddeley.

Back at the hotel, Lightning read Mater's note.
Lightning hadn't wanted Mater to leave, but at least
now he wouldn't have to worry about Mater getting
into trouble.

In fact, Mater was helping Finn and Holley. Together they looked at a holographic photo that was on the device that Torque had given Mater. Mater said the photo was of a poorly made, gas-guzzling engine with some expensive new parts. But he didn't know who the engine belonged to.

Finn, Holley and Mater flew to Paris. Finn was hoping a black-market parts dealer named Tomber could tell them who the mysterious engine in the photo belonged to.

Mater explained that the engine belonged to a Lemon – a car that didn't work right. Gremlins, Pacers, Hugos and Trunkovs were all types of Lemons. Tomber said there was going to be a big meeting of Lemons in Porto Corsa, which was also the location of the next World Grand Prix race!

Lightning and his crew soon
arrived in Italy for the race. Their
first stop was Luigi and Guido's
hometown. Everyone came out to
greet them!

Meanwhile, Holley was disguising Mater as one of the Lemons' tow trucks so that he could sneak into the meeting. She gave Mater lots of cool spy gadgets too!

The next day before the race in Porto Corsa, Lightning admitted to Francesco that he really missed Mater.

Little did Lightning know, Mater was actually nearby. With his disguise, Mater had made it into the Lemon meeting held at a casino. Holley and Finn were positioned outside, listening in on the action through Mater's headset.

Professor Z introduced the Lemons to their Big Boss who appeared on a TV screen. But only his engine was visible – the same engine in Torque's photo!

The Big Boss said that once Allinol was proven lethal, all cars would use gasoline again. Then the Lemons, who controlled the oil reserves, would finally get the wealth, respect and power they deserved!

As the Big Boss spoke, Grem and Acer aimed the camera at Carla Veloso, the race car from Brazil.

Finn raced to the top of the tower to stop Grem and Acer. As he leaped over a crevasse to get to the Lemons, a helicopter captured him with a giant magnet!

Finn was taken away and Grem and Acer continued to harm even more cars. Their next victim was Shu Todoroki, the racer from Japan.

Shu's engine exploded!

Meanwhile, at the race track finish line, Lightning shot across for the win.

By now, everyone thought Allinol was to blame for the crashes. But Lightning insisted he would use Allinol in the final race.

The Big Boss heard Lightning's statement and gave the order to destroy Lightning.

Mater tried to leave and warn his friend, but his disguise disappeared. He tried to escape using his spy gear!

But before Lightning could spot Mater, the Lemons hauled him away. The next thing the tow truck knew, he, Finn and Holley were tied up inside a giant clock called Big Bentley. They were in London, England, the location of the final race!

Grem and Acer told Mater that they had planted a bomb inside Lightning's pit at the race.

After the pair left, Mater escaped and rushed to save his friend.

Finn and Holley soon broke their bonds, too. Suddenly they realised that the Lemons let Mater escape on purpose. The bomb was actually on Mater and he was heading straight to Lightning! Holley quickly extended her wings and burst through the clock face!

As Mater arrived at the pits, Finn radioed to say the bomb was on him.

Mater tried to leave the pits before Professor Z could detonate the bomb.

Professor Z spotted Holley from his viewing box and fled. Now it was up to Grem and Acer to do away with Lightning so that all Lemons could finally rise to power!

Holley flew off to help Mater, while Finn went after the Professor.

59

The criminal attempted to escape, but Finn lassoed the Professor with cables and captured him!

Finn arrived with Professor Z and ordered him to deactivate the bomb.

Professor Z informed Finn that only the one who activated the bomb could turn it off – and that was *not* the Professor.

All at once, the other Lemons arrived to get rid of Finn, Holley, Mater and Lightning. But, the Radiator Springs crew came to the rescue and defeated the Lemons with some fancy moves.

Suddenly, Mater figured out who the Lemons' Big Boss was. He flew straight to Buckingham Palace with Lightning.

When Mater landed at the palace, Finn and the guards warned him to keep the bomb away from the Queen.

Mater quickly explained that the engine in the photo belonged to Miles Axlerod. Axlerod was the Big Boss and the biggest Lemon of all!

Mater went on to explain that Axlerod made Allinol look dangerous so everyone would give up alternative fuels and go back to using gasoline. Then all the Lemons would get rich!

Axlerod was trapped and had no choice but to deactivate the bomb. Mater had saved the day! No one was prouder of him than Lightning.

The Queen thanks Mater by knighting him for his bravery!

Soon Mater, Lightning and the rest of their friends were back at home preparing for a big event: The Radiator Springs Grand Prix. Even Finn and Holley came to watch.

They wanted Mater to join them on another spy mission, but the tow truck politely refused. He belonged in Radiator Springs with his best buddy, Lightning.

Mater used his spy rockets one last time and zoomed onto the race course. Together, the two best friends left the others in the dust!